The Whale
In Lowell's Cove

Written and Illustrated by
Jane W. Robinson

Down East Books
Camden, Maine

A percentage of the proceeds from the sale of this book will be donated to whale rescue organizations by both author and publisher.

ISBN 0 89272 308 1
Library of Congress Catalog Card Number 91-77670

Color separations, printing, and binding
Done in Hong Kong through Four Colour Imports

9   8   7   6   5   4   3   2   1

Down East Books, P.O. Box 679, Camden, Maine 04843

Author's Note

In the summer of 1990, a young humpback really did swim into Lowell's Cove in my town of Harpswell, Maine. This is my story of her unusual month-long stay there.

Pogies are major characters in this book. Their real name is Atlantic menhaden. Menhaden are small silvery fish with iridescent overtones on their scales. They are plankton eaters that like the warm, shallow water in Maine's coves and inlets during the summer. They swim in vast schools, which makes them easy to catch in a seine net—or in the broad, open mouth of a humpback whale.

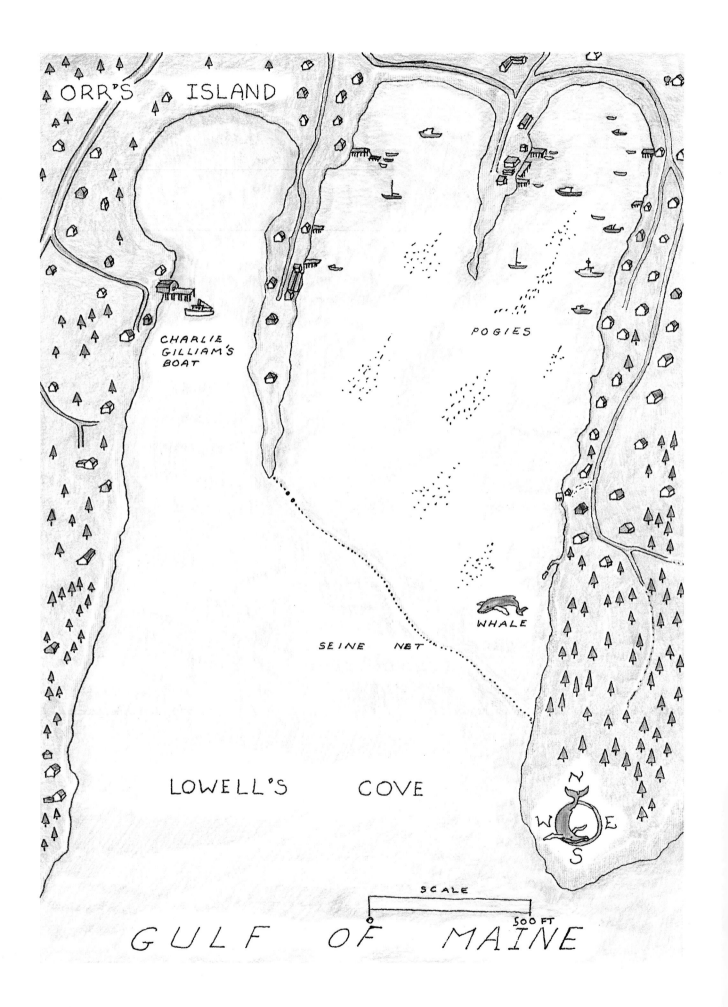

ORR'S ISLAND

CHARLIE
GILLIAM'S
BOAT

POGIES

WHALE

SEINE NET

LOWELL'S COVE

N
W E
S

SCALE
500 FT

GULF OF MAINE

Lowell's Cove is one of many small harbors and inlets in the town of Harpswell on the Maine coast. It is cold and wind-tossed in winter, but the warm summer sun finds it glittering with blue wavelets and full of boats.

In June, schools of pogies swim into the cove to feed. Fishermen then close off the mouth of the cove with a long seine net. The top edge of the net is held up by floats. The bottom is held down by lead weights that rest on the floor of the cove. A "door" in the net about eight feet deep allows the fishing boats to enter and leave.

Trapped behind the net, the pogies spend their summer in the cove. They have plenty to eat and room to move about. Each morning, a school of them are netted up and sold to the local lobster fishermen for bait.

One quiet day at the beginning of July, a whale appeared in Lowell's Cove. There she swam, *inside* the long seine net that closed off the cove from the deep ocean. Perhaps she had been chasing a big school of pogies that swam into the cove. Now, both the pogies and the whale were inside the net.

People were astounded! A whale right here in Lowell's Cove! They told all their friends. More and more people came by boat and by car. They all wanted to see the humpback whale. She was even on television!

She was a young humpback whale, only one and a half years old. Still growing, she was already thirty feet long. Her sleek body was a glossy blue-black and her graceful flippers were a lovely white.

Everyone thought she was so big and so beautiful! People came in the afternoons and evenings to see her dive and hear her blow when she surfaced for air. They could watch her quite well even from the shore.

In the early mornings the cove was peaceful. The silver-pink water lay smooth and calm. Silent boats slept at their moorings. Most of the people in the cottages were still asleep in their beds. The whale, wide awake, fed on the pogies trapped inside the net. She would lunge up, her mouth full of many, many pogies and gallons and gallons of water. Then she'd push all of the water out through her strainer-like baleen plates. The water would flow out through the plates, but the pogies would get caught behind the baleen. She'd swallow them and swim after more.

Since humpback whales only eat during the summer half of the year, this young whale had a lot of eating to do. She needed to eat about 1,200 pounds of pogies each day. Maybe the cove was a good place for a growing young whale. It was full of fish!

Whale experts from the New England Aquarium came to make sure the whale was all right. They were especially concerned because humpback whales are an endangered species. Was it good for her to live in such a small cove, they wondered. Was she healthy? She looked thin to them.

The experts knew she'd left her mother less than a year ago. Young whales often have difficulty catching enough to eat. Maybe she needed the pogies trapped inside the seine net. They watched her feeding. She certainly seemed to be getting plenty of food.

Some of the whale watchers said they had seen the whale leave the cove, so maybe she was not actually trapped by the net. The aquarium people decided to leave her in the cove for now, but return later to check on her.

So the whale stayed inside the net in Lowell's Cove.

←FRINGE   WHALE FACTS

SOME SPECIES OF WHALES DO NOT HAVE TEETH. INSTEAD, BALEEN PLATES HANG FROM THEIR UPPER JAW. MADE OF KERATIN, LIKE YOUR FINGERNAILS, THE BALEEN PLATES HAVE A FRINGED INNER EDGE.

TO FEED, A WHALE GULPS IN A MOUTHFUL OF WATER AND FISH. THEN THE WHALE PUSHES THE WATER OUT THROUGH THE BALEEN, WHICH ACTS LIKE A STRAINER. THE FISH ARE TRAPPED INSIDE AND SWALLOWED WHOLE.

Soon many, many boats full of excited people were crowding in to see the whale. They didn't mean any harm, but most of these visitors did not know anything about whales. Some even tried to poke her with their oars!

The weekends were the worst of all. Because of all the boats, there wasn't enough room for a thirty-foot whale to come to the surface and breathe. She might be cut by a boat's propeller. The whale was very young and very trusting. She didn't know that she was in danger!

Still the whale stayed inside the net in Lowell's Cove.

WHALE FACTS

IT IS POSSIBLE TO TELL HUMPBACK WHALES APART BY THE PATTERNS ON THE UNDERSIDE OF THEIR FLUKES (TAILS). SCIENTISTS NAME THE INDIVIDUAL WHALES AND KEEP TRACK OF THEM BY THEIR FLUKE PATTERNS.

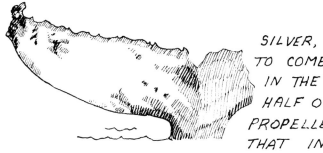

SILVER, ONE HUMPBACK WHO USED TO COME TO THE GULF OF MAINE IN THE SUMMER, WAS MISSING HALF OF HER FLUKE. A BOAT PROPELLER MAY HAVE CAUSED THAT INJURY.

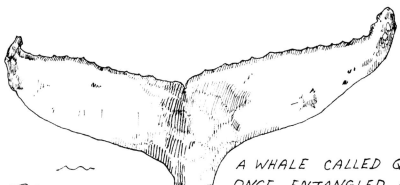

A WHALE CALLED QUIXOTE WAS ONCE ENTANGLED IN OFFSHORE FISHING GEAR, AND WAS FEARED DEAD. BUT HE SURVIVED, AND SCIENTISTS WERE GLAD TO SEE HIM SWIMMING FREELY IN 1990. THE MARK ON HIS FLUKE LOOKS LIKE DON QUIXOTE ON HIS HORSE.

Some of the people in town worried about the whale's safety. They called the National Marine Fisheries Services in Gloucester, Massachusetts. They called Greenpeace in Boston, Massachusetts. They called the Maine State Fisheries Office in Augusta. "Protect the whale!" they said. "Someone is going to hurt her by accident! We need help here in Lowell's Cove!"

All of the agency people got together to think of a way to protect the whale. They knew that since the United States government has declared humpback whales an endangered species, people are not allowed to "harass or otherwise harm" them on purpose. But what could they do to keep people from *accidentally* hurting the whale?

Finally a state patrolman thought up a great idea: the state could pass a special temporary law to stop people from using boats in the cove for as long as the whale stayed there. The only boats allowed in were those of the fishermen coming in to buy pogies.

From then on, the whale had plenty of room. People could still watch her from shore or from boats *outside* the cove.

In the early mornings, Charlie Gilliam, who owned the seine net that was stretched across the cove, sold pogies to the lobstermen for bait. The lobstermen were very careful as they brought their boats into the cove. They motored slowly, keeping a sharp eye out for the whale's exact location.

Charlie grew fonder and fonder of the whale as the days passed. Some mornings, when he first came into the cove, she would swim over to greet him. She recognized the sound of his engine starting up.

A daily routine evolved. The whale would be up early catching pogies. Almost as early, Charlie would come out to his boat. He'd net a batch of pogies and sell them to the arriving lobstermen. Later, in the afternoon and evening, other people would crowd into the cove to see the whale from shore.

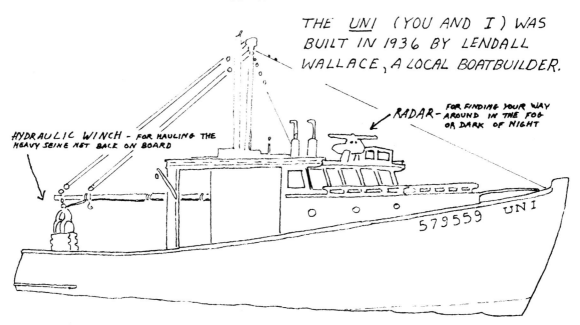

CHARLIE'S BOAT

THE UNI (YOU AND I) WAS BUILT IN 1936 BY LENDALL WALLACE, A LOCAL BOATBUILDER.

RADAR - FOR FINDING YOUR WAY AROUND IN THE FOG OR DARK OF NIGHT

HYDRAULIC WINCH - FOR HAULING THE HEAVY SEINE NET BACK ON BOARD

579559 UNI

UNLIKE MANY WORK BOATS TODAY, THE UNI IS POWERED BY A QUIET GASOLINE ENGINE RATHER THAN A NOISY DIESEL ONE. CHARLIE NEEDS A QUIET BOAT SO HE CAN COME UP CLOSE TO SCHOOLS OF FISH WITHOUT SCARING THEM AWAY.

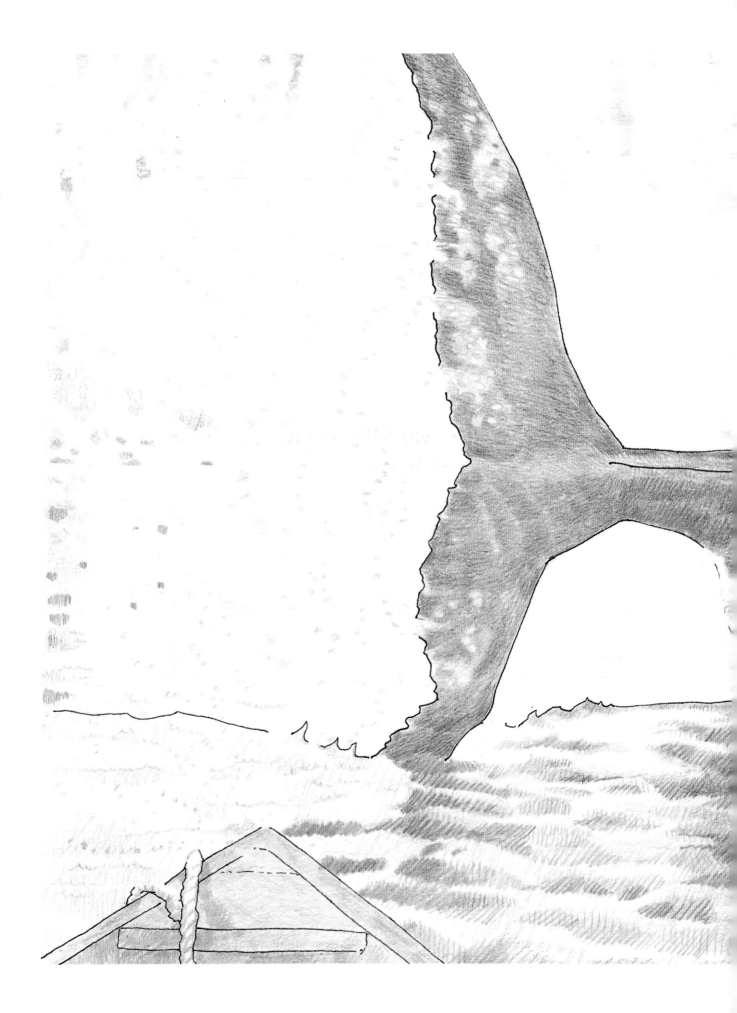

The whale ate pogies and played. She did all the things a young and happy humpback whale should do. She would throw herself out of the water and into the air, then land on her back with a loud *kersplash!* She'd roll over on her side and flap her flippers on the water. She'd stand on her head underwater, throw her tail up, and slap the water with a loud *smack!*

When she was tired from play, she'd nap out next to the net facing the deep, open ocean where she'd come from.

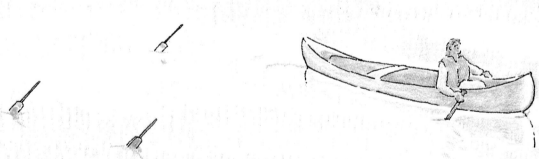

Once in a while, visitors who didn't know about the special law paddled into the cove in their canoes and kayaks. Fascinated, they'd glide right up to the whale. The whale's friend, Charlie, would see them and sigh. He'd motor over in his big pogie boat and tell them to go outside the net. They always did once they understood why boats were not allowed in the cove.

Three whole weeks went by.

The whale ate.

The whale played.

And when she wasn't doing anything much, she floated next to the net facing out to the deep, open ocean where she'd come from.

The whale experts came back to check on her. "She spends a lot of time looking out to sea," they said.

One morning the whale was feeding up among the boats and lobster buoys at the head of the cove. Charlie and his crew were there, too, looking for pogies.

Suddenly there was a commotion in the water in front of Charlie's boat. The whale had gotten her tail flukes entangled in the long rope that connected one of the lobster buoys to its trap down on the bottom. Charlie's crew all rushed on deck in alarm. They were all greatly relieved to see the whale pull herself free! When she did, the rope rubbed sore, raw patches on either side of her flukes.

She was lucky she pulled free. Sometimes young whales get tangled in fishing gear and drown! Maybe a small cove full of boats moored by ropes and lobster buoys connected to traps with ropes wasn't such a safe place for a young whale after all.

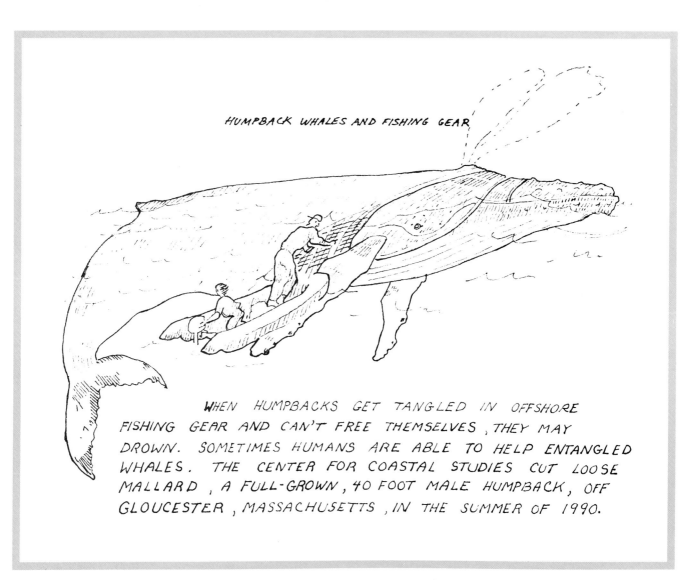

HUMPBACK WHALES AND FISHING GEAR

WHEN HUMPBACKS GET TANGLED IN OFFSHORE FISHING GEAR AND CAN'T FREE THEMSELVES, THEY MAY DROWN. SOMETIMES HUMANS ARE ABLE TO HELP ENTANGLED WHALES. THE CENTER FOR COASTAL STUDIES CUT LOOSE MALLARD, A FULL-GROWN, 40 FOOT MALE HUMPBACK, OFF GLOUCESTER, MASSACHUSETTS, IN THE SUMMER OF 1990.

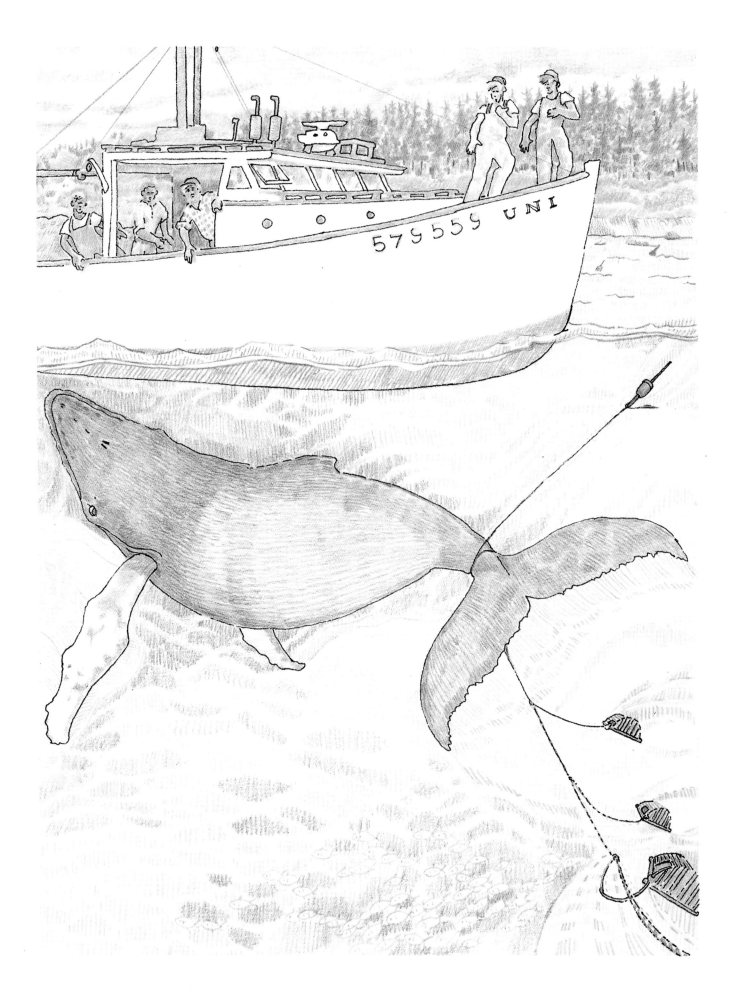

The experts at the New England Aquarium heard about the whale's narrow escape. "This isn't good," they said.

Another weekend came, and so did even more people, all wanting to see the whale. She seemed happy. She threw herself out of the water and breached. She flipped her tail and slapped the water. She napped near the surface with the top of her head and her blowhole rising out of the water every ten minutes or so for a good, deep breath. But she spent a lot of time by the net facing toward the deep, open ocean that was her home.

People began to ask, "Can she *really* come and go if she wants to?" Was this little cove a good place for a whale?

WHALE   FACTS

WHALES BREATHE AIR JUST AS OTHER MAMMALS DO. A WHALE'S BLOWHOLES (NOSTRILS) ARE ON THE TOP OF ITS HEAD. STRONG MUSCLES KEEP THE BLOWHOLES TIGHTLY CLOSED WHILE THE WHALE IS UNDER WATER.

THE BUMP AROUND THE BLOWHOLES IS A SPLASH-GUARD THAT KEEPS THE WATER FROM GOING INTO THE HOLES AS THE WHALE BREATHES IN.

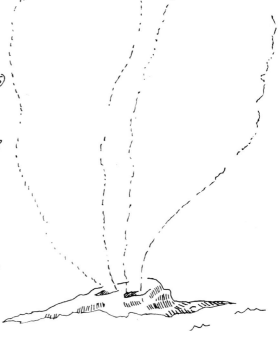

WHALES DO NOT BREATHE UNCONSCIOUSLY, AS HUMANS DO. THEY HAVE TO THINK ABOUT THEIR BREATHING.

WHEN THE WHALE BREATHES OUT, ITS BREATH CONDENSES, MAKING A "SPOUT". HUMPBACKS HAVE A V-SHAPED SPOUT BECAUSE THEY HAVE TWO BLOWHOLES.

Then, one morning when Charlie boarded his boat, the whale did not swim up to greet him. Where was she? She wasn't feeding. Had she left the cove?

No! Charlie heard a very quiet "blow" from out near the net. Something was wrong! Charlie hurried over in his big pogie boat. He found the whale all tangled up in the long seine net!

Charlie sped back to the dock for his crew and a skiff. They carefully edged up alongside of the whale. Talking softly to calm her, they pulled the net away from her with long gaffs. The whale didn't struggle—she let them free her. Thank goodness Charlie had found her before she drowned!

After this, the whale experts realized something had to be done. There were too many hazards for a young whale in Lowell's Cove. The whale had stayed there for a month. During that time she had eaten lots of pogies and charmed hundreds of people with her play. But now she had been tangled in fishing gear twice and nearly drowned. It was time for her to go.

A few people were still convinced that the whale came and went when she wanted to. "If you let her out, she'll come right back," they declared. But other people wondered whether she really could leave voluntarily. Maybe when the whale seemed to be gone, she was only quietly napping out by the net and was hard to see.

WHALE   FACTS

HUMPBACKS ARE NOT THE ONLY BALEEN WHALES IN THE GULF OF MAINE. OTHER BALEEN WHALES THAT COME THERE IN THE SUMMER TO FEED ARE:

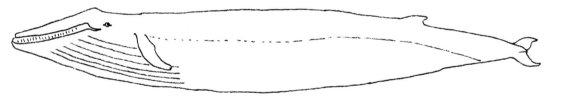

FIN WHALE 70 TO 80 FEET LONG

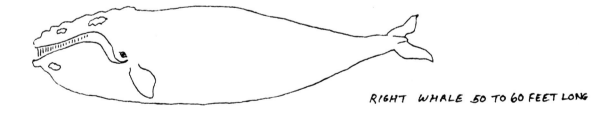

RIGHT WHALE 50 TO 60 FEET LONG

MINKE WHALE 30 FEET LONG

The whale experts listened to both sides and then decided that the whale should be released. "Maybe she'll come back in, but maybe she won't," they said.

The whale experts were concerned because they knew that all humpback whales in the North Atlantic migrate south in September. This whale needed to be free to join the other whales. If she had a chance to leave, would she go? Would she come back? No one knew.

The fishermen had a problem. They were afraid they would lose all their pogies if the net was taken down to release the whale. It was only the first of August. They needed to sell pogies for another month or two.

The fishermen and the whale experts talked it over. Together, they came up with a plan.

PURSE SEINING   (POGIE FISHING)

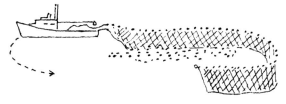

AFTER THE FISHERMEN LOCATE A BIG SCHOOL OF POGIES, THEY RUN A NET AROUND THE SCHOOL.

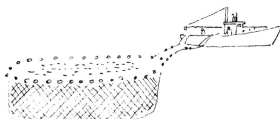

NOW THE SCHOOL IS INSIDE A CLOSED CIRCLE OF NET, WHICH IS OPEN AT THE BOTTOM.

NEXT, THE "PURSE LINE" IS DRAWN TIGHT TO CLOSE UP THE BOTTOM EDGE OF THE NET, MAKING A BAG, OR "PURSE."

Margaret Anne

FINALLY, THE NET IS HAULED UP PARTWAY, MAKING THE PURSE SMALLER SO THE FISH ARE PACKED CLOSER TOGETHER. NOW THE POGIES CAN BE DIPPED UP EASILY TO BE SOLD FOR BAIT.

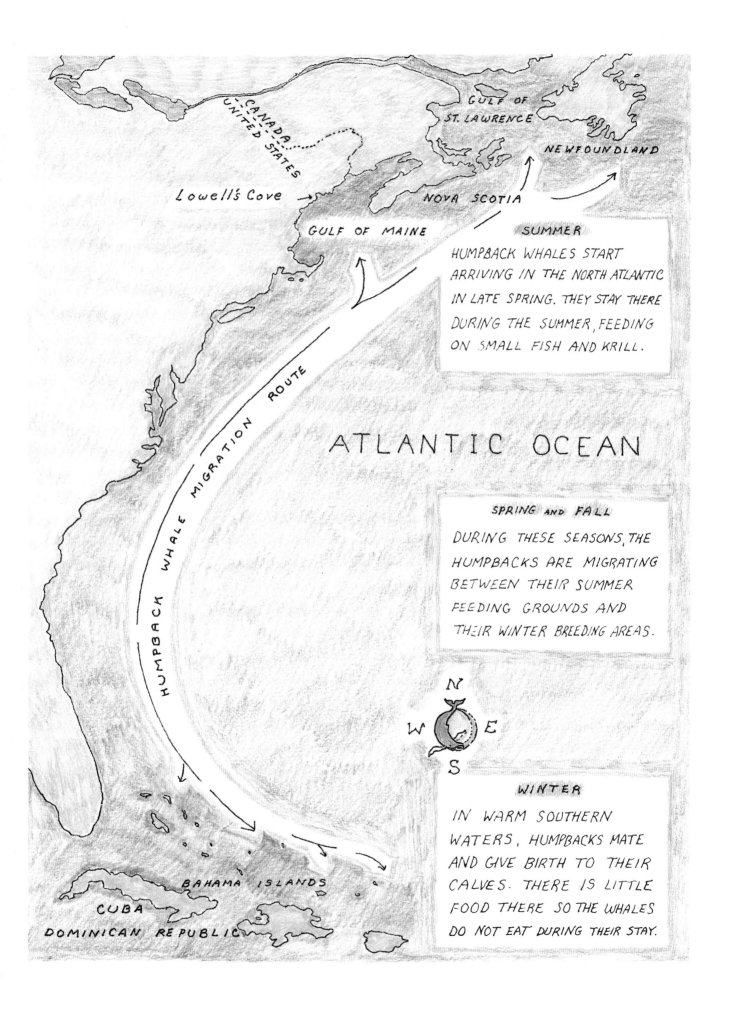

CANADA
UNITED STATES

GULF OF
ST. LAWRENCE

NEWFOUNDLAND

Lowell's Cove →

NOVA SCOTIA

GULF OF MAINE

SUMMER

HUMPBACK WHALES START ARRIVING IN THE NORTH ATLANTIC IN LATE SPRING. THEY STAY THERE DURING THE SUMMER, FEEDING ON SMALL FISH AND KRILL.

ATLANTIC OCEAN

HUMPBACK WHALE MIGRATION ROUTE

SPRING AND FALL

DURING THESE SEASONS, THE HUMPBACKS ARE MIGRATING BETWEEN THEIR SUMMER FEEDING GROUNDS AND THEIR WINTER BREEDING AREAS.

N
W E
S

WINTER

IN WARM SOUTHERN WATERS, HUMPBACKS MATE AND GIVE BIRTH TO THEIR CALVES. THERE IS LITTLE FOOD THERE SO THE WHALES DO NOT EAT DURING THEIR STAY.

BAHAMA ISLANDS

CUBA

DOMINICAN REPUBLIC

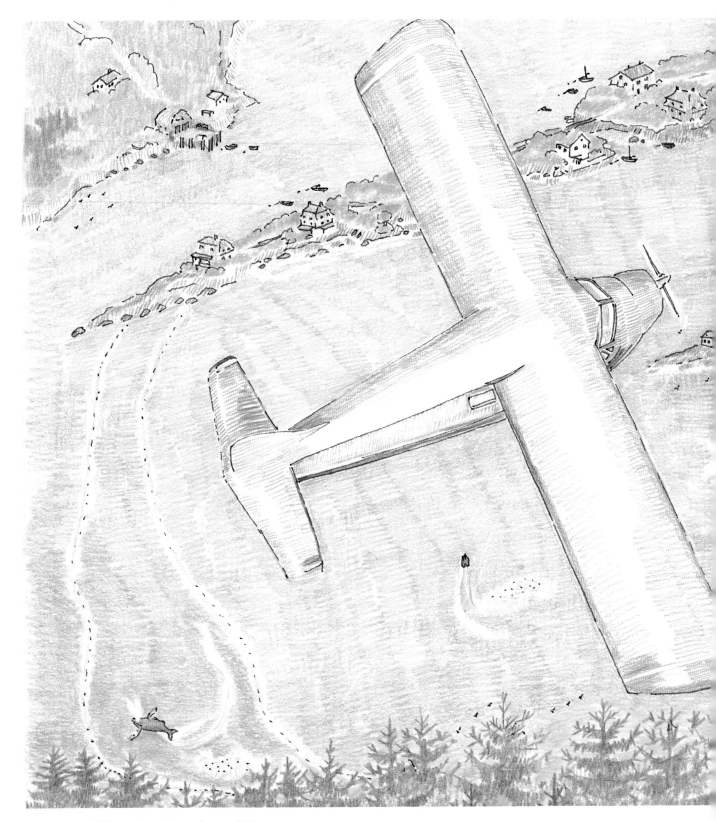

Here is what they did.

They waited until the whale had finished her early-morning feeding. She swam out beside the net to nap. A spotter plane pilot, who had been sent up to watch the pogies, radioed down the good news: Most of the schools were at the head of the cove, far away from the whale.

Quickly, one of the fishermen scooted behind the whale in his dory, pulling a second net across the cove.

That part of the plan had worked. The pogies were all safely inside the new net. The whale was between the two nets. She woke up and swam about. She knew there were now two nets.

Next, the fishermen and whale experts made sure no boats were outside the cove that might frighten the whale. Then, slowly and carefully, the fishermen weighted down a section of the outer net with hundred-pound weights.

Everyone waited, holding very still. What would the whale do?

She swam up to the opening in the net. She knew something was different! Frightened, she swam away a bit. Then she came back to the net.

She stuck her head through the opening. Then she swam backward and dove out of sight! What was going to happen? What would she do? Did she really want to stay in the cove?

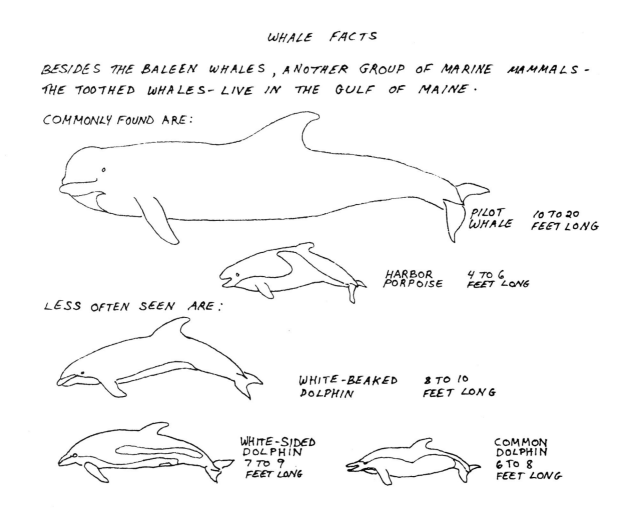

WHALE FACTS

BESIDES THE BALEEN WHALES, ANOTHER GROUP OF MARINE MAMMALS—THE TOOTHED WHALES—LIVE IN THE GULF OF MAINE.

COMMONLY FOUND ARE:

PILOT WHALE 10 TO 20 FEET LONG

HARBOR PORPOISE 4 TO 6 FEET LONG

LESS OFTEN SEEN ARE:

WHITE-BEAKED DOLPHIN 8 TO 10 FEET LONG

WHITE-SIDED DOLPHIN 7 TO 9 FEET LONG

COMMON DOLPHIN 6 TO 8 FEET LONG

Suddenly the whale surfaced *outside* the seine net! Everyone cheered! She took a big breath and dove again. The fishermen hurried to pull up the weights and let the net rise. The whale experts leaped into their boats, ready to follow the whale. They wanted to see where she would go.

The whale headed straight out to sea as fast as she could swim. She breached completely out of the water and came down on her back.

Kersplash!

Huge splashes of ocean water glistened in the early sunlight each time she landed.

Kersplash!

Kersplash!

Over and over again she breached, swam, then breached again.

Kersplash!

Kersplash!

Kersplash!

The young whale left all the people and their boats and their fishing gear and the pogies in Lowell's Cove far, far behind her. She swam out, far out, into the deep, open ocean where she belonged.

Somewhere out in the Atlantic Ocean swims a young humpback whale who once stayed for a month in a tiny Maine harbor. Now she is back in her own deep, blue, watery world.

May she grow strong and wise. She is already sweet and gentle.

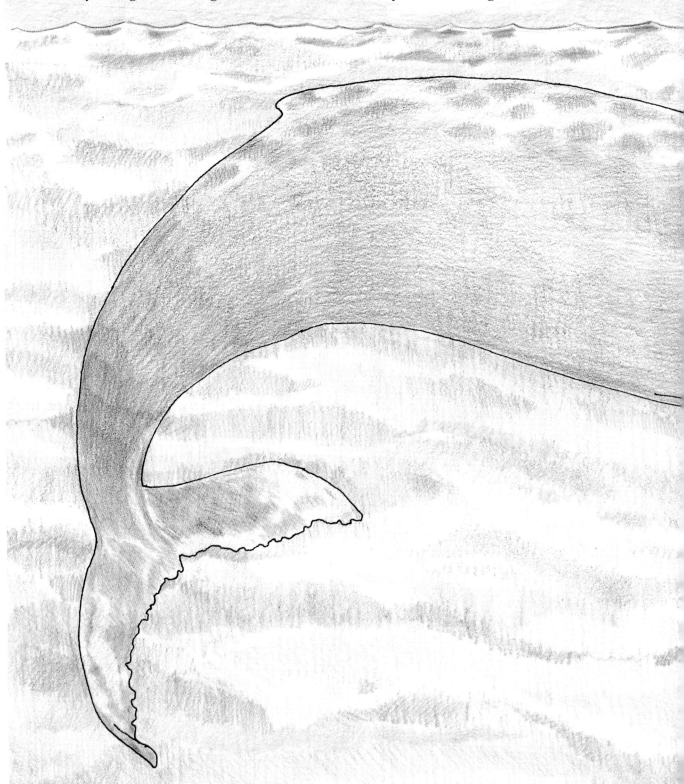

She touched many hearts during her brief stay in Lowell's Cove.

The whale who stayed in Lowell's Cove swam off into the Gulf of Maine on August 3, 1990. Whale experts followed her for over an hour, until she had swum past the last island. She breached over and over and headed out to sea.

We know she is a female because the Coastal Studies scientists were able to collect some tiny skin pieces that were shed as the whale splashed back into the water when she breached. They sent the skin samples to Per Pasboll, a scientist in Denmark. By looking at DNA from the skin cells, he determined the whale's gender.

The identity of this particular humpback remains a mystery. Photographs of her fluke pattern have been carefully checked against all the fluke patterns on record at the Center for Coastal Studies. Hers did not match any in their files. Now that they have her fluke pattern recorded, they will be able to give her a name and identify her again when she is next sighted.

Charlie Gilliam

The whale's fisherman friend, Charlie Gilliam, lives at Lowell's Cove on Orr's Island, Maine. Charlie comes from a long line of fishermen, beginning with Emore Gilliam, who fished out of Lowell's cove a century ago. Fishermen like Emore caught mackerel and bluebacks (a big sea herring) in seine nets similar to the ones Charlie uses to catch pogies. Both Charlie's father, Charles, Sr., and his uncle, Raymond, also fished in Lowell's Cove. Raymond was the first owner of Charlie's boat, the *UNI*.

Charlie is also a professional Country and Western musician. He has played on the same concert bill as such famous performers as Hank Snow and Ernest Tubb. As lead singer and guitar player in his band, The Coastliners, Charlie recently sang his new version of the old favorite, "There She Goes." The song's new title was, "The Whale of Casco Bay."

> There she goes.
> She's swimming away,
> And each flip she makes
> Brings heartache my way.
> She won my heart
> And I guess it shows.
> I'll miss her so,
> There she goes . . .

Whale Experts

The New England Aquarium has been rescuing marine mammals since 1968. The motto of their Marine Animal Rescue and Rehabilitation program is, "To provide humane care to sickly, injured, or distressed marine animals." Whales, dolphins, seals, sea turtles, and even sea birds have been helped by their program.

Greg Early, the scientist who visited Lowell's Cove most often, oversees the aquarium's rescue and rehabilitation program. He leads a network of scientists, veterinarians, and volunteers throughout the Northeast. Greg and his staff kept behavioral observations on the Lowell's Cove whale. He worked with the National Marine Fisheries Service and local fishermen to decide how to release the whale without losing the fishermen's valuable pogies.

Greg also was in charge of the rescue of two groups of stranded pilot whales on Cape Cod in 1986 and 1990. Five of those pilot whales were brought back to the New England Aquarium, where they were rehabilitated and eventually released back into the wild. The three from 1986—Tag, Notch, and Baby—have since been seen swimming with a pod of other pilot whales in the Cape Cod area. The other two whales, Maushop (named after the Indian god of whales) and Melaena (meaning "black"), were released into the ocean in June 1991.

Colleen Coogan, one of the other whale experts in this book, is Protected Species Biologist with the National Marine Fisheries Service. The NMFS is responsible for the conservation and protection of marine mammals, including whales, dolphins, and seals.

The Center for Coastal Studies, also on Cape Cod, sent two of the whale experts mentioned in this book: Dr. Charles Mayo and David Mattila. The Center is a nonprofit organization dedicated to research, education, and conservation of marine life. Since 1984, their Whale Rescue Program team has disentangled numerous marine mammals, including whales, from fishing gear. The Center also responds to reports of marine mammal strandings.

You can help assure that whales stay free and healthy by adopting a whale yourself. One organization through which you may adopt an Atlantic humpback is the International Wildlife Coalition. Write to them at:

> Whale Adoption Project
> International Wildlife Coalition
> 634 North Falmouth Highway
> P.O. Box 388
> North Falmouth, MA 02556-0338

Acknowledgments

There are many people without whom this book would not have been possible. I am especially grateful to the many photographers who generously shared their work with me: Sarah Schmidt, Gary Bonaccorso, Paul Cunningham, Lloyd Thompson, Charlie Gilliam, Jennifer Bove, Judy Schmidt, and David Mattila of the Center for Coastal Studies.

Everyone needs moral support and courage in an endeavor. I got mine from The Maine Writers and Publishers Alliance; Clare Howell; Sarah Schmidt; Dotte Larsen; my mother, Pat Robinson; and, especially, Ron Chipman.